THE DAY THE EARTH SHOOK

10 Publishing

a division of **10** of those.com

Have you ever felt the ground shake?

Did you quake?   Did you tremble?

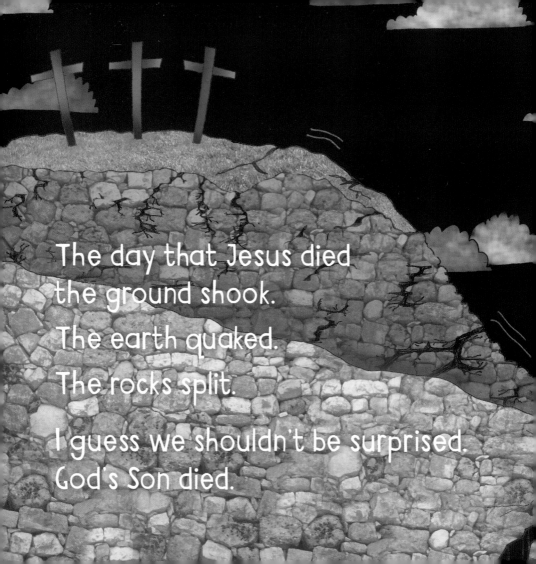

The day that Jesus died
the ground shook.

The earth quaked.

The rocks split.

I guess we shouldn't be surprised.
God's Son died.

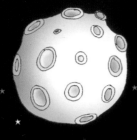

After all, it was Jesus who measured the ground.

Jesus who arranged the earth.

Jesus who shaped the rocks.

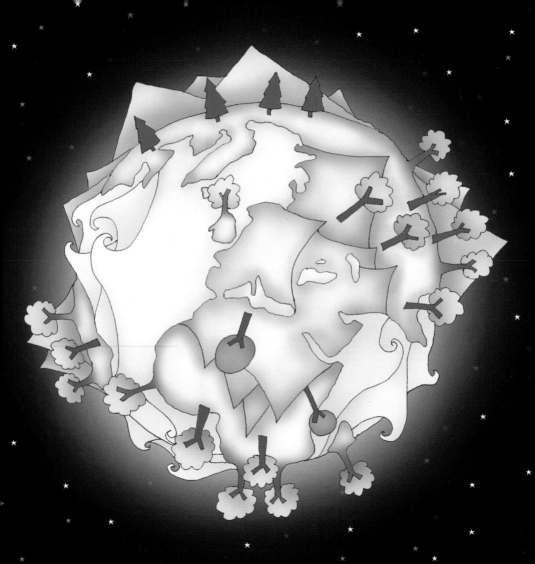

The day that Jesus died
the ground shook.
The earth quaked.
The rocks split.

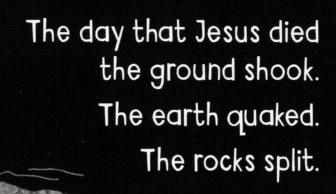

I guess we shouldn't be surprised.

God's Son died.

No wonder the ground
couldn't stay still.

Even the brave soldier guarding Jesus was scared.

Only someone really powerful can make the earth shake. Only someone really strong can cause rocks to break apart. The soldier looked up at Jesus. He looked down at the broken rocks. He thought about the earthquake. And he realised something.

This was no ordinary man.
This was God.
God's own Son.

And the soldier said,

"Surely he was the Son of God!"

The day that Jesus
died the ground shook.
The earth quaked.
The rocks split.

The Son of God died.

Shocking. Staggering. Shattering.

But it was the only way.

The Sinless for the sinful. The Maker for the made.

The Right for the wrong. The Maker for the made.

For us. What love!

The day that Jesus died
the ground shook.

The earth quaked.

The rocks split.

I guess we shouldn't be surprised.
God's Son died.
No wonder the ground
couldn't stay still.

So, maybe, like the ground,
we should shake a little bit.

Perhaps we should tremble.

After all, what Jesus
did was amazing.

What Jesus did was super powerful,
super strong love in action!

SUPER
POWERFUL,
SUPER
STRONG
LOVE

Hey shaky, quaky trembler!
Don't worry...
that's not the end of the story...

That's the brilliant
news of Easter.

Jesus is alive!

We can know and we can say,

"Jesus is the Son of God!"

You can find out more about how we can
be friends with Jesus by reading the Bible.
The Easter story is in Matthew chapter 27.

For Katherine and David whom we love
and who show us Jesus' love in action.

And for Dawn, who wanted her name in a book!

The Day the Earth Shook

Text and Illustrations © 2016 Helen Buckley and Jenny Brake.

Published by 10Publishing, a division of 10ofThose Limited.
ISBN 978-1-910587-56-0

Typeset by Diane Warnes.
Printed in the UK.

10ofThose Limited, Unit C Tomlinson Road, Leyland, PR25 2DY
Email: info@10ofthose.com
Website: www.10ofthose.com